D1588145

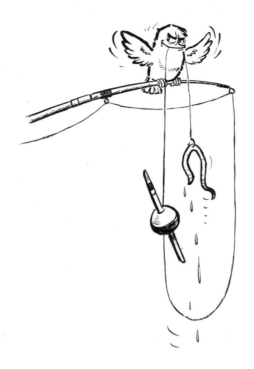

TO MY DAUGHTERS
PENNY JUNE AND
DEBBIE JOY.

it's a bird's life

by **HARGREAVES**

MUSEUM PRESS

First published in book form in Great Britain by Museum Press Limited
26 Old Brompton Road, London, S.W.7

1965

Reprinted, 1966

The Artist and the Publishers wish to express their thanks to
Messrs. Bradbury, Agnew & Co. Ltd., for permission to
reproduce these drawings, all of which first appeared in PUNCH.

PRINTED IN GREAT BRITAIN
BY OFFSET
UNWIN BROTHERS LIMITED
WOKING AND LONDON
R.3424

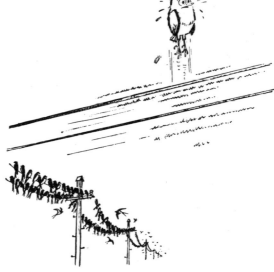

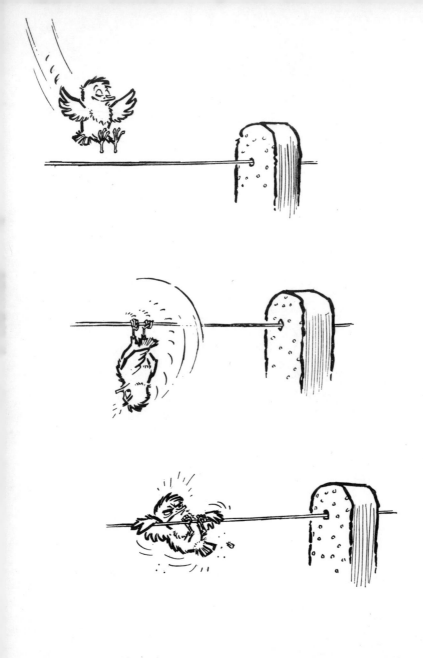

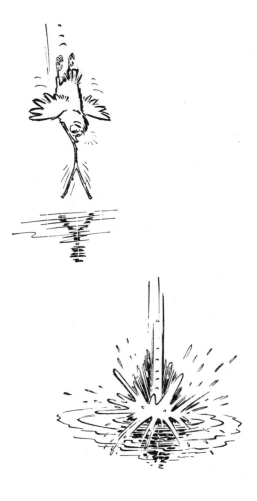

★ "... Lost my way ... going back after winter in the sun, you know — the usual Western racket ... aimed for Britain ... our homing instincts not as good as Russian birds — Russian birds always lay first eggs — Russian birds sing best ... what ARE the pickings like at the salt mines, anyway? ... worms a bit salty, eh? ha ha!"

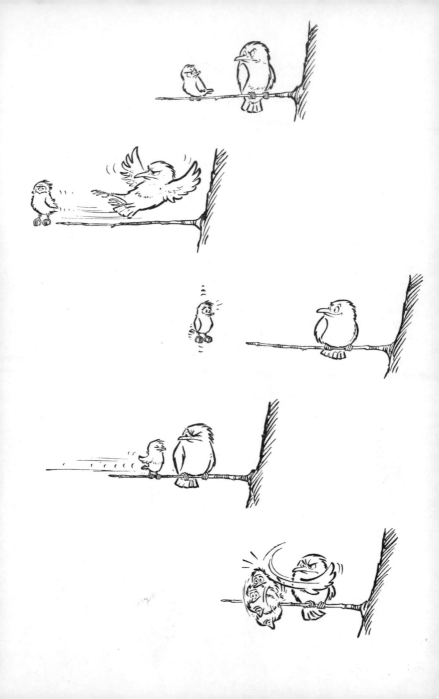

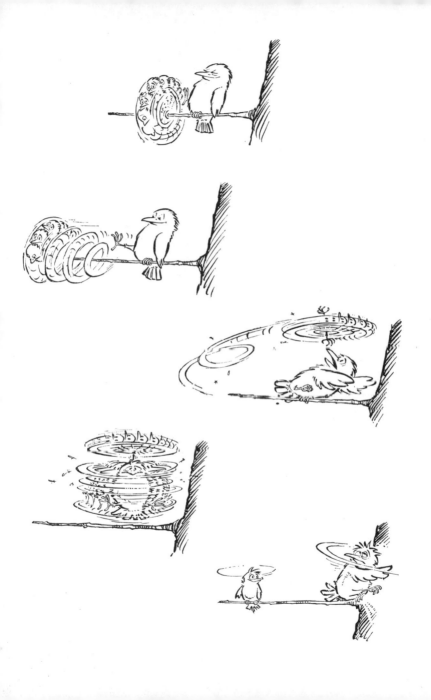

BOTANICAL
GARDENS

TEAK

(TECTONA GRANDIS)

RANGOON

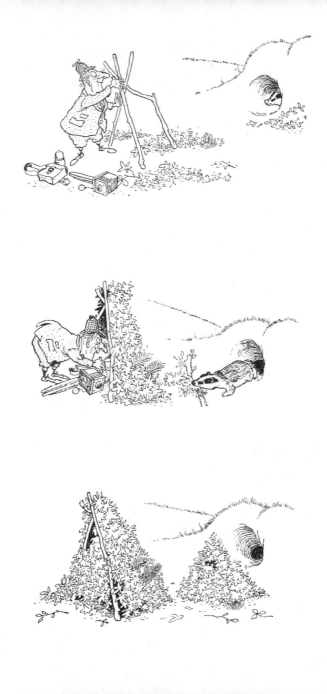